Little RIDDLERS

A Pocketful Of Poetry

Edited By Donna Samworth

First published in Great Britain in 2020 by:

 Young**Writers**

Young Writers
Remus House
Coltsfoot Drive
Peterborough
PE2 9BF
Telephone: 01733 890066
Website: www.youngwriters.co.uk

Printed and bound in the UK by BookPrintingUK
Website: www.bookprintinguk.com
YB0452L

FOREWORD

Dear Reader,

Are you ready to get your thinking caps on to puzzle your way through this wonderful collection?

Young Writers' Little Riddlers competition set out to encourage young writers to create their own riddles. Their answers could be whatever or whoever their imaginations desired; from people to places, animals to objects, food to seasons. Riddles are a great way to further the children's use of poetic expression, including onomatopoeia and similes, as well as encourage them to 'think outside the box' by providing clues without giving the answer away immediately.

All of us here at Young Writers believe in the importance of inspiring young children to produce creative writing, including poetry, and we feel that seeing their own riddles in print will keep that creative spirit burning brightly and proudly.

We hope you enjoy riddling your way through this book as much as we enjoyed reading all the entries.

CONTENTS

Roderick Tejeda (8)	69
Reeha Shahzad	70
Maria Huzaifa	71
Raheem Brotherson Morris (8)	72
Ella-Marie McQueen (8)	73
Firsha Firos Kapattakath Ottayil (8)	74
Mariah (10)	75
Asha Bogdanowicz (10)	76
Tyrell Green	77
Chris Grant (8)	78

Eden Park Primary School Academy, Brixham

Lexie Elliott (7)	79
Lydia Temple (7)	80
Albie Williams (7)	81
Jonah Adamson (7)	82
Nafisa Jannat (7)	83

Heron Hill Primary School, Kendal

Evie McAvoy (6)	84
Luke Mason (6)	85
Clara Jones (6)	86
Elana Adgie (6)	87
Sophie Annand (6)	88
Matilda Cramphorn (6)	89
Isla Newell (6)	90
Reggie Bainbridge (6)	91
Myla Bigland (6)	92
Phoebe Evans (6)	93
Alexander Shaw (6)	94
Olivia Pickering (6)	95
Dexter Calvert (6)	96
Sophie Galea (6)	97
Evie Fothergill (6)	98
Kayla Pitura (6)	99
Lily Pearson (6)	100
Phoebe Mackereth (6)	101
Alec Birch-Rushworth (6)	102
Max Carter (5)	103
Amelia Mawson (6)	104

Jessica Fishwick (6)	105
Seren Birch (5)	106
Kassius Venning (6)	107

King Charles CE Primary School, Falmouth

Charlotte Mackenzie (7)	108
Emily Searle (7)	109
Ruben Kahane (7)	110
Braxton-Heath Boots (7)	111
Ethan Hill (7)	112
Beatrice Cavender (6)	113
Sam Kahane (7)	114

Purley CE Primary School, Purley On Thames

Annabelle Parker (7)	115
Freya Eldred (6)	116
Brandon Pollard (7)	117
Lewis Tovey (7)	118
Phoebe Tovey (6)	119

Shirland Primary School, Shirland

Elsie Butcher (6)	120
Sophie Vickers (6)	121
Chelsea Neilson (6)	122
Millie-Grace Ryan (6)	123
Joseph Lee (6)	124
Harry Fletcher (6)	125
Keira Vickers (6)	126
Finley Bradshaw (6)	127
Logan Jones (6)	128

St Barnabas Primary School, Oxford

| Robin Arbuthnott (6) | 129 |

St Dunstan's RC Primary School, Moston

Mia Brailsford (6)	130
Ermiyas Kifle (6)	131
Fiyinfoluwa Ibitoye (6)	132
Finley Lamour (6)	133
Hosieo Selemon (6)	134
Rae Toner (5)	135
Emilia Ajayi Usman (6)	136
Charlotte Lodge (6)	137
David Omanua (6)	138
Bernice Agbontaen (6)	139
Oscar Whittaker (6)	140

The Phoenix Primary School, Laindon

Zach Sproit (7)	141
Georgia McDonald (7)	142
Jake Maynard (7)	144
Damian Phillips (7)	145
Oliver Rose (7)	146
Summer Riggs (6), Aleksandra Padron (6), Imani Hills Powell (7), Freya King (6), Ava (7) & Kadian Richardson (6)	147
Danilas Subonis (7)	148
Nkiere Along (6), Tadas Vaisnoras (7), Devon Regan (6), Charley & Adanna Nwaiwu (6)	149
Frankie Fayers (7)	150
Alexis-Rose White (7)	151
Archie Stevens (7)	152
Bella Fairclough (6)	153
Daniel Ojedele (7)	154
Ollie Amiable (7)	155
Kyra Kudjoe-Swan (7)	156
Faye Simons (7)	157
Lilyray Cahill (7)	158
Natalie Caddy (7)	159
Riley Hayter (7)	160

The Ursuline Preparatory School, Ilford

Isla McNaughton (6)	161
Maliha Dearing (6)	162
Isla Rose Pearson (6)	163
Rishaan Sharma (6)	164
Leyla Pearson (6)	165
Zakariya Patel (5)	166

Unity College Nursery, Blackpool

Harry Hodgson (6)	167
Jacobe Cunningham (7)	168
Lucas Algar (6)	169
Jayden McCreadie (7)	170
Lola Mitchell (6)	171
Darci-Mae Gibson (6)	172

THE POEMS

My First Riddle

This is my riddle about an amazing animal
What could it be? Follow the clues to see!

This animal has tusks on its body
And its colour is grey.
This animal has four feet.
It likes grass and fruit and bark to eat.
The jungle or the zoo is where it lives,
Its favourite thing to do is play and splash
all day.
This animal has two ears.
It makes trumpet, squeaking and chirping
sounds for you to hear.

Are you an animal whizz?
Have you guessed what it is?
It is...

Answer: An elephant.

Leo William Draper (4)

Jumping Philip

What could I be?
Follow the clues to see!
My large eyes, bigger than my stomach,
look like kiwi fruit
My bat-like ears can hear sounds that
humans can't hear
My blob-tipped fingers and toes can grip
almost anything
I am the size of a tennis ball
I am awake all night long and I don't get in
trouble with my mum
I use my frog-like back legs to jump super
high
I can jump higher than a big red London
bus!
I am named after the country I was born in
What am I?

Answer: I am a Philippine tarsier.

Leon Akladious (5)

My Elegant Swimmer

I have a cover which is as white as a brand-new snowflake coming out of a frigid cloud But I'm not a white pillow.

What I eat with is as orange as scrumptious, mouth-watering marmalade.

I can be terrifying if you do not take care of me with a flame of friendship.

I am as beautiful as the red rope of love between my family and me.

I am the largest member of my family members.

I ride through the crystal-like, adequate and azure waters.

What am I?

Answer: A swan.

Safa Hossain

What Animal Is It?

It has a white horse-like body,
Its not really been seen by anybody

It has huge wings to fly off its feet,
It likes berries and nuts to eat

It lives in the deep, dark woods,
I would love to be there if I could

Its favourite thing is to show off its horn,
No one knows when or where it was born

It's full of magical powers,
I can listen to its stories for hours!

Are you an animal whizz?
Have you guessed what it is?

Answer: It's a unicorn!

Tanya Joy (6)

The Splashing Showman!

I am shiny and as dark as the night when wet,
But fluffy and squishy when dry,
I have long, white, wiry whiskers that help me detect prey and navigate,
My favourite food is yummy fish from the salty sea,
Although I look as lazy as a lion I can put on a fantastic show like the circus,
I can clap and wave and make a big splash,
I am happy in the water and when showing off to a noisy cheering crowd,
Can you guess what I am?

Answer: A sea lion.

Jack Curtis (7)

Long Living, Slow Swimming

I am pale white, but I am so dirty I look green.
I am also rarely seen.
Predators of me, there's few.
If you touch me, I might attack you.
I am an aggressive sea creature.
Releasing a chemical is my attractive feature.
I live in the deep briny blue.
Swimming in translucent waters, so my prey I can pursue.
What am I?

Answer: A Greenland shark.

Jonathan Atkins (7)

Flamingo Riddle

My name starts with 'F' and ends with 'O'
Meaning of my name is "Fire"
I am very beautiful but don't have teeth
I feed my babies with milk made in my
throat
I am pink and my milk is pink too
I keep my babies in a giant water nursery
I usually pose with one foot tucked under
my body
Who am I?

Answer: A flamingo.

Vaibhavika Dhamgaye (5)

The Clever Tree Climber

I am about the same size as your large pet cat,
Although you would never see me sitting on the mat,
My red face is as cute as a bunny,
And my bushy tail is kind of funny.
I eat bamboo, awake in the night,
And people come to me and fight,
I'm endangered because they are destroying my home
Can't they just leave the trees alone?
What am I?

Answer: A red panda.

Rosie Geary

Roar

I am a social carnivore
I always live in a group
I do not drink every day
That is a skill of mine!
When hunting I am clever but my wife is better
How annoying!!!
You can hear my voice from 8 km away
I am under the threat of becoming endangered
I am the second-largest cat species in the world.
What am I?

Answer: A lion.

Amr Mohamed Khaled Eldaly (6)

Sea Life

I'm sailing across the Pacific Ocean
I see whales and sharks splashing around in the water
What a wonderful sight
Lots of creatures are swimming around in the ocean, which we cannot see
Deep, deep down, what could there be?
Colossal squid, octopus, anglerfish and many more.
I get to the coast and on the beach, I see litter so we need to sweep, sweep, sweep!

Phoebe Dacombe (7)

The Sky Soarer

As I fly from high above
Soaring through the sky like a dove
I am white and fluffy
Sometimes big, but always fluffy
In different colours, I grow
The people I see down below
As I travel around the world
So many sights to see
The whole world is saved just for me
I come in different shades
White, blue and grey.
What am I?

Answer: A cloud.

Ainsley Tsanga (5)

A Terrible Lizard

We come in different sizes-
Some of us are small,
Some of us are ginormous.
We once ruled Earth,
But we didn't wear a crown.
We are closely related to the chicken,
Although that wouldn't stop one of us
eating one!
There are many different types of us.
What are we?

Answer: Dinosaurs.

William Goodfellow (6)

Red Warning

I start my life as an egg on a leaf
I can live for as long as a year
I am part of the beetle family
When I'm grown up I can fly
I use my antennae to taste and smell
My bright red wings make predators think
I'm poisonous
You might have fun counting my spots
What am I?

Answer: A ladybird.

Cora Ham (6)

Jump, Jump - You'll Never Be As High As Me

I jump high into outer space
My baby is tucked away in a very safe place
When I am a baby I don't have fur
I am an animal, but not the kind that will purr
When I jump up I see monkeys in the tree
I can jump about 10 foot high and I go weeeee
Can you guess what I might be?

Answer: A kangaroo.

Krisen Bhamrah

Sophie's Marvellous Animal Riddle

This is my marvellous animal riddle,
Do you know what I am?
I live under the sea.
I have no legs.
I have a long nose and I can curl my tail.
I can be lots of different colours.
I share part of my name with an animal that has four legs and says 'neigh'.
Have you guessed what I could be?

Answer: A seahorse.

Sophie O'Neill (6)

Jessica's Fantastic Animal Riddle

This is my fantastic animal riddle,
Do you know what I could be?
I boing up and down to move around.
I am soft and fluffy to touch.
I have four legs.
I like to eat crunchy, orange carrots.
I can live in the wild or be a pet in your house.
I have long, floppy ears.
Have you guessed what I am?

Answer: A rabbit.

Jessica O'Neill (7)

The Hunter

I am a hunter that likes to catch its prey
I have sharp claws on my paws
I live in places like a showering rainforest
My teeth are as sharp as a vampire's teeth
Watch out! I am crazy!
You can't see me because my patterns help me camouflage.
What am I?

Answer: A tiger.

Ashley Davies (7)

Sea Gymnast

I have a body as smooth as silk
My eyes are as white as pearls
My tail is like a fast superpower
I have fins like pyramids sitting on my body
My mouth is as long as a pencil
I speed through the ocean like a lightning strike
I am very shy
What am I?

Answer: A dolphin.

Isabella Werling (7)

Ancient Animal

I am big and small, I can be any size
I can be a carnivore, herbivore or omnivore
I lived way before humans lived here
I am scary with big teeth and spikes
I can walk, I can fly, I can swim
I've been extinct and paleontologists found me
What am I?

Answer: A dinosaur.

Salahuddin Khan (5)

A Famous Grid

This is a table that has no chairs
It has things that are everywhere
It has silver, it has gold
It has something to measure how hot or cold
There are hard, shiny metals but no diamond ring
The building blocks of everything
What is it?

Answer: *The periodic table.*

Alannah George (5)

The Camouflaging Creature

I am as blue as the night sky
I am as small as a slimy, sticky slug
I can camouflage as well as bright colourful starfish
My arms are like brown creaky branches
We eat ourselves
If you hold us we will sting you like a bee
What am I?

Answer: A blue dragon.

Aliza Khalid (6)

I'm Clear And Blue

When the sun shines I am blue
When I crash onto the rocks I make a noise
Lots of creatures call me their home
Lots of things like to float on me
Lots of birds like to fly over me
When you fall into me you will be cold
What am I?

Answer: The sea.

Molly Gibbon (7)

The Carrot Muncher

I am small and cute
I have fur that is as soft and comfy as a blanket
I have fur that is white, black and grey
I like to eat carrots and leaves with my sharp teeth
I like to bounce around everywhere
My ears are over 2 3/4 inches long
What am I?

Answer: A bunny rabbit.

Catherine Thompson (6)

The King Of The Savannah

I'm a king but I don't live in a castle
I have a mane but I am not a horse
I have a tail but I'm not a dog
I am yellow and orange like the sun
I hunt but not alone
I'm proud of my pride
What am I?

Answer: A lion.

Harvey Pearson (7)

Mr Tall Neck

I eat leaves out of very tall trees
I live in Africa
I have brown spots all over my body
I've got a long tongue but I'm not a frog
I drink water once every 2-3 days
I am a quick runner
What am I?

Answer: A giraffe.

Isshani Das (6)

What Am I?

I live close to the greeny-yellow seabed
I eat huge sea creatures
I have powerful fins
I have razor-sharp teeth
I have gills on my sides
Some of my species include the Great White
and Hammerhead
What am I?

Answer: A shark.

Robbie Vere (7)

Friendly Bouncer

You can find me in the deep blue sparkly oceans.
I am a carnivore.
I have a nose shaped like a bottle.
I am playful like a little kitty.
If you touch me, I will not hurt you.
I can jump out high in the sky like a bouncy ball.
What am I?

Answer: A dolphin.

Matas Poska

Something Fishy

I am as long as a slithery snake
I have 20 dangerous teeth
I am an underwater animal
My mouth and teeth are as sharp as a knife
I am giant and I am grey
I live in the salty seas of Australia
What am I?

Answer: A shark.

Aila Lemmetyinen (6)

The Mystery Of Colour

I am all colourful.
I am made from sunshine and rain.
I am sometimes way up in the clouds.
If someone tries to find my treasure, I just move away.
But if you are lucky, you might find a pot of gold at the end of me.
What am I?

Answer: A rainbow.

Isabelle Everton (6)

Lion Piper

My mane is thick as a chain
My claws are sharp as a sword
I have a jaw as deadly as fangs
I have yellow fur like the sun
I move in packs like a cat
My eyes are as blue as the sea
What foe am I?

Answer: A lion.

Madhav Nambiar

Mister Long Legs

I have extremely skinny legs,
My face is as round as a beach ball,
Crawling around is enjoyable,
I dislike children who trample on me,
Weee! I'm swinging in the air,
My home is made out of stretchy string,
What am I?

Answer: A spider.

Malaikah Iqbal

My Animal

It can fly like an eagle
It is as strong as a stone
It likes to eat a big strawberry ice cream
It blows fire in rainbow colours
It is pretty like a ballerina
It is as cute as me
What is it?

Answer: A dragon.

Malina Merosu

Beach

I'm very soft
I'm at the beach
If you get tired lie down on me
You can build castles out of me
When the waves splash I get very wet
When you get hungry have a picnic on me
What am I?

Answer: Sand.

Aurora Johnson (7)

Things Of Nightmares

I am soft and hard.
I am stinky but tasty.
I am round or a triangle.
I quite often come from France.
I am produced from cow, sheep and goats milk.
I can come warm, cold or waxy.
What am I?

Answer: Cheese.

Sidney Green (7)

The Predator

I have a long tail and razor-sharp teeth
I have a strong sense of smell, which could be described as electric.
I need to keep moving in order to breathe.
I have gills.
My dorsal fin helps me balance.
What am I?

Answer: A shark.

Idrees Mohammad (5)

Tiny Pet

Tiny is so cute
She runs in the park
She sleeps in the bed like a baby
Children love to play with her
She is soft like a blanket
Her name is Tiny
Do you know what she is?

Answer: She is my tiny cat.

Raameen Jaiyana (6)

Bird Crossing

I live near water and I am a wild bird
I cleverly catch fish and let the water out
I am white like a seagull
My name begins with a 'P'
I have beautiful, nice wings
What am I?

Answer: A pelican.

Poppy Sandamas (6)

The Snowy Cat

I am as white as the snow
I love to climb mountains
I live in Asia
I eat goats and sheep
I have fur and spots
I have four legs and a tail
I am a big cat.
What am I?

Answer: A snow leopard.

Jayden Higiu (6)

Wonderful World

I smell with my antennae
I like my beautiful patterns
I like to stay in my warm home
I am little
I drink sweet pollen
I am a minibeast
I have a long tongue
What am I?

Answer: A butterfly.

Anashe Isla-Jo Muskett (6)

Up Above

I have the beautiful moon
The shining sun
I have the clear-white clouds
The twinkly stars
I have all the weathers and the birds
I am blue, white and dark blue
What am I?

Answer: The sky.

Zahrah Balal (9)

Riddle

I am spiky and I'm beautiful.
I smell very sweet and have green leaves.
Everyone buys me to plant in their garden.
I have colourful flowers.
I can grow very big and can prick people.
What am I?

Answer: A rose.

Anton Velichko (7)

What Am I?

Everyone loves playing with me
When they play with me I bounce up and
down
I come in different colours
I come in a round shape
I am fun to play with for everyone both
young and old
What am I?

Answer: A ball.

Naazneen Shonibare (7)

Waving In The Wind

I am as green as a jumping frog
I am spiky
I fall in the wind
I go crunch, crunch, crunch
There are loads of me
I can change colour when I grow old
What am I?

Answer: A leaf.

Imogen Siddiky (5)

Colorful Inside

I have three wings.
There is water in front of me.
There is a lady sitting.
I am in a big city.
I have glass in front of me.
I am ancient.
I'm full of decorated objects.
What am I?

Answer: *The Louvre.*

Adèle (6)

What Amazing Animal Am I?

This is my riddle,
What can I be?
I live under the sea.
I have big sharp teeth.
My head looks like a hammer.
Lots of people are scared of me.
Do you know what I am?

Answer: A hammerhead shark.

Ethan O'Neill (4)

The High Hopper

I can jump really high
I am small
I have soft teeth
I can't bite hard figs
I'm not scary
I have six legs
I make a noise
What am I?

Answer: A grasshopper.

Noel Odiase (6)

Magic Horn

Magic horn
I look like a horse
I have a magic horn
I can float in the sky with no wings
I have colourful hair and a colourful tail
I have four hooves
And I have a big body
What am I?

Answer: A unicorn.

Isabel Fallon

I Am A Crustacean

I am red like an apple
I walk on the sea floor
I can leave my shell
My teeth are in my tummy
My tail is very muscly to fight off predators
What am I?

Answer: A lobster.

Denny Kaya (6)

All Around

I am all around
I make no sound
I always go with my spiky boots to get
closer and closer
But they think I am a monster and want me
gone
What am I?

Answer: The Coronavirus.

Aadhya Sarkary (4)

You Find Me Everywhere

I can be different colours.
You sometimes step on me.
You put your bottom on me.
I help you stay upright.
I'm lots of shapes and sizes.
I can be comfy or not.
What am I?

Answer: A chair.

Emi Wheatley (7)

Give A Try

My name starts with 'E'
And I am a big grey beast
I love my food
And banana is my favourite feast
Can you guess who am I?
Come on give it a try!
What am I?

Answer: An elephant.

Amaira Deotale (6)

Riddle

It looks like a happy smile
It sounds like a squeeze
It smells like perfume
It feels safe and warm
It tastes sweet
What is it?

Answer: A kiss and cuddle with Mummy.

Lola Hibbins (5)

Look At Me

I can be shiny and colourful
I am something you wear
I can be your friend or enemy
I have hands
I like numbers
My face can change
What am I?

Answer: A watch.

Isabel John (5)

The Small Monster In The Corner

I am very small
I have eight legs
I like cobwebs
I like to eat flies
I don't like the rain
Some people are scared of me
What am I?

Answer: A spider.

Muhammad Ismail (5)

The Flying Mystery

I come out at night
I can see without light
My feathery wings are nice
I like to eat mice
I can hoot and it sounds like a flute.
What am I?

Answer: An owl.

Ava Mathurin (6)

Under The Sea

I am a girl
I am also a fish
I am as kind as my mum
I have beautiful red hair
I am as small as a doll
Who am I?

Answer: Ariel, the little mermaid.

Anni Lemmetyinen (5)

A Real Dinosaur Or Not

A real dinosaur or not
Once upon a time, there was a little cute
dinosaur
He liked to sleep more and more
The sleepy dinosaur had a snoring fame
The riddle is to guess what is his name?

Eva Deotale (6)

Catch Me

I am found
I can go up
I come in lots of colours
I am good for sport
You can throw me
You can catch me
What am I?

Answer: A ball.

Emmet Burgess (5)

Clues

I'm full of clues,
And also mysteries,
The answer could be palace, dinosaur or candy,
I can be easy and I can be tricky.
What am I?

Answer: A riddle!

Hareem Bhatti (7)

What Is It?

It looks sharp
It sounds like music
It smells like seaweed
It feels wet
It tastes salt
What is it?

Answer: *The sea.*

Mark Omeje (6)

What Am I?

I am a meat-eater,
I have sharp teeth like razors,
I have soft fur,
I have a massive mane.
What am I?

Answer: A lion.

Rion Rudaj (6)

What Am I?

I have shiny white teeth,
Dark black eyes,
Dark blue fins,
Light blue skin,
And I live in the water.
What am I?

Binyamin Bhamji (7)

The Mighty Warrior God

I am as strong as a lion
I have deep scars all over my big-boned
body
I wear solid gold armour all over
I am a man
I did something extremely awful that makes
me feel incredibly heartbroken
My stepmum is an evil person who wants to
get rid of me
My dad is a famous ancient Greek god
I am a caring, loving person so when I do
terrible deeds I make myself do brutal
challenges
They might even lead to my death!
I still do them so I can forgive myself
I have killed animals that people have said
cannot be killed
Who am I?

Abisola Adebiyi (9)
Chestnut Park Primary School, Croydon

A Hero Demi-God

I am the most popular, powerful god-like hero from Greek mythology.
I am super powerfully built with divine strength and incredible abilities.
My muscular, bulging arms can perform deeds no mortal can.
As tall as a giraffe, I enormously stand out among the humans of the Earth.
Cast under the wicked spell, my entire family were butchered with my own hands.
Even though I'm not guilty of their deaths, grief and remorse fill my already broken heart.
Desperate to atone for my sins and regain immortality, I accept to carry out a dozen soul-breaking tasks.

With my protruding arms, as quick as lightning, the dozen soul-breaking tasks are overcome.

Who am I?

Keziah Joy Berchie-Wellars (9)
Chestnut Park Primary School, Croydon

A Mystery God

I am strong, friendly and have nice hair
I wonder what you think over there
I look like the Hulk but I don't bite
I lost something that gave me so much delight
I am willing to get it back that has something to do with twelve
Do you know who I am and what I look like boys and girls?
I did something wrong but am now doing what is right
I want to say sorry and I think you are alright
We could be a family again if you like
When I was a baby I was a god indeed
Then some evil villains took that away from me
Now I am off to do my thing

This has to do with the number twelve
I'm from ancient Greece
Who am I?

Elliana
Chestnut Park Primary School, Croydon

God Almighty

I stand tall, proud and confident
I have more power than any mortal can
imagine
My reputation precedes me as everyone is
aware of the punishments I have placed
upon others
As beautiful and wealthy as I am, my selfish
and jealous ways shine through
My enemy is the strongest I know as he
defeats the labours I throw
Who am I?

Imani Rhoden
Chestnut Park Primary School, Croydon

The Legend Of The Moon

I'm the mother of all cats
I was a fierce lioness but later turned into a cat
I'm known as the daughter of Ra and Isis
I married Phta, a fierce god with the face of a lion
I am sometimes called the soul of Isis
I have a son named Maahes
Who am I?

Roderick Tejeda (8)

Chestnut Park Primary School, Croydon

Swishing Waters

Crops grow healthy because of me
Swish goes the thing that I need to help the crops grow
My beard is a long black worm
I am like the ice of the Arctic
I am the god that lots of people worship
I dance like the flowers that move side to side
Who am I?

Reeha Shahzad
Chestnut Park Primary School, Croydon

Queen Of The Jungle

I look like a woman with war fire on my
hand
I have a sun disc like Ra the sun god
I create fire and I have a green hand
My eyes are red like blood
My war fire food bistro is everything
I never lost my war fire
Who am I?

Maria Huzaifa
Chestnut Park Primary School, Croydon

Wrapped Up

I'm in charge of something important
My head is covered in black
I have a necklace and gold jewellery
I hold a stick and never let go
I have something in my hand
I'm a wise man
Who am I?

Raheem Brotherson Morris (8)
Chestnut Park Primary School, Croydon

Queen Of Beauty

I am a caring goddess and I look after the sick

My husband looks like Shrek and lives in the Underworld

I have a burning round ball of fire on my head

Swish swish, my hair sways side to side

Who am I?

Ella-Marie McQueen (8)

Chestnut Park Primary School, Croydon

The Sky

I am a bird and I have the head of a bird
I have the head of a woodpecker - *click, click, click*
I am a god of the up
I am the god with a white and red clour on my hat
Who am I?

Firsha Firos Kapattakath Ottayil (8)
Chestnut Park Primary School, Croydon

Who Am I?

I have bright yellow hair
I have strong muscles
My dad is the king of Olympus
I murdered my family
I didn't mean to
I buried the Hydra's head in a hole
Who am I?

Mariah (10)
Chestnut Park Primary School, Croydon

Monster

I am snakey and slithery
I am abnormal
A great hero had slain me
Home is where I am toxic
The people run from me
Many fear me
I have an immortal head
Who am I?

Asha Bogdanowicz (10)
Chestnut Park Primary School, Croydon

Wise Old Man

I have a long, pointy beak
It is longer than a pole and sharper than a knife
Sometimes I look like a baboon
My skirt is white and yellow
I give people wisdom
Who am I?

Tyrell Green
Chestnut Park Primary School, Croydon

Who Am I?

My ears point north
My hair is blue
I have sapphire bracelets
I have a head like a black dog
Who am I?

Chris Grant (8)
Chestnut Park Primary School, Croydon

I Like Red

I am a jolly person
Big and round
I live in a magical world
Cold all year round
I fly through the night
But you can't hear my jingling bells
I bring fun and toys
I hear your happy yells
I say ho, ho, ho in a happy voice
I leave your present, what a good choice!
Who am I?

Answer: Santa Claus.

Lexie Elliott (7)
Eden Park Primary School Academy, Brixham

Bat Pigs

We have big, bat ears
We have a squished-up fat face
We are very silly
When we lie down we have back legs like a chicken
We love our beautiful humans
Our blue ball is our favourite
We love walking in the leafy green woods
Who are we?

Answer: Ronald and Luna, the French bulldogs.

Lydia Temple (7)
Eden Park Primary School Academy, Brixham

Crackling Bubble Maker

Born from a tiny stick
I am a forest's doom
Crackling bubble maker
A warm, cosy room
Red, yellow, orange, white
So very, very bright
I could make Antarctica melt
What am I?

Answer: Fire.

Albie Williams (7)

Eden Park Primary School Academy, Brixham

Friend

I can be seen but not heard
I come in all shapes and sizes
I am in every home
I can make you smile or cry
I am shiny and your friend
When you are alone
What am I?

Answer: A mirror.

Jonah Adamson (7)
Eden Park Primary School Academy, Brixham

Light

I am tall when I am young
I'm short when I am old
I burn bright
What am I?

Answer: A candle.

Nafisa Jannat (7)
Eden Park Primary School Academy, Brixham

Master Of Dark

I am dark all over my body
I have a big tail
I live on the surface
You can draw me
I sometimes eat fish
Some of us are wild
I have green eyes
I do whatever I want
I am small
I am camouflaged in the dark
I am cuddly
What am I?

Answer: A black cat.

Evie McAvoy (6)
Heron Hill Primary School, Kendal

A Colourful Treat

I am cold as an ice cube
I taste nice
I make you shiver when you eat me
You eat me when it's hot
You need to eat me before I melt
I can be any colour in the rainbow
What am I?

Answer: Ice cream.

Luke Mason (6)
Heron Hill Primary School, Kendal

Italian Delights

I am yellow, wiggly and long
I am delicious
I come from Italy
I am in Lady and the Tramp
Sometimes you can put cheese on me
I come in a bowl
What am I?

Answer: Spaghetti bolognese.

Clara Jones (6)
Heron Hill Primary School, Kendal

Fairy Tale

Sometimes witches capture me
I live in a castle
I wear a crown
I have a pink sparkly dress
I like to sing
I like to dance with a prince
What am I?

Answer: A princess.

Elana Adgie (6)
Heron Hill Primary School, Kendal

Whiskers

I am a milk drinker
I love to sleep outside
I have sharp claws
I can be black, brown or white
Dogs chase me
I make two different sounds
What am I?

Answer: A cat.

Sophie Annand (6)
Heron Hill Primary School, Kendal

Ice Animals

I am a bird but I don't fly
I live on ice
I eat fish
I go in the water
I swim
Daddy keeps me warm when I'm an egg
What am I?

Answer: A penguin.

Matilda Cramphorn (6)
Heron Hill Primary School, Kendal

Wet Sloppy Kisses

I am the colour of sand
I make a woof noise
You will find me in a house
I have four legs
I am friendly
I feel fluffy
What am I?

Answer: A puppy.

Isla Newell (6)
Heron Hill Primary School, Kendal

What Am I?

I have spots
I am a herbivore
I am taller than an elephant
I have long legs
I have a longer neck
I live in Africa
What am I?

Answer: A giraffe.

Reggie Bainbridge (6)
Heron Hill Primary School, Kendal

Pretty Wings

I have wings
I can fly
My wings are pretty
You cannot touch me
You don't often see me
You see me in gardens
What am I?

Answer: A butterfly.

Myla Bigland (6)
Heron Hill Primary School, Kendal

Pretty Flight

I can fly but I am not always real
I don't glide
I am not an animal
I am pretty
I am little, I am similar to people
What am I?

Answer: A fairy.

Phoebe Evans (6)
Heron Hill Primary School, Kendal

Monster Of The Zoo

I have green skin
I live in the zoo and shiny places
I like rivers
I have four legs
I have a long tail
I am long
What am I?

Answer: A lizard.

Alexander Shaw (6)
Heron Hill Primary School, Kendal

Water Creep

You might find me in a pond
I am very very small
I feel slimy and wet
I look dark black
My mummy is like a toad
What am I?

Answer: A tadpole.

Olivia Pickering (6)

Heron Hill Primary School, Kendal

Scale

I can roll in a ball
I have yellow armour
I eat termites
I live in Africa and China
I look like an armadillo
What am I?

Answer: A pangolin.

Dexter Calvert (6)
Heron Hill Primary School, Kendal

The Flying Insect

I am colourful but my face is black
I am beautiful
I don't make sound
I have wings
I am an insect
What am I?

Answer: A butterfly.

Sophie Galea (6)
Heron Hill Primary School, Kendal

Vegetable

I am orange
I am a vegetable
You might find me in the fridge
You can eat me raw and cooked
I am bumpy
What am I?

Answer: A carrot.

Evie Fothergill (6)
Heron Hill Primary School, Kendal

What Am I?

I am green and small
I am yummy
I grow in orchards
I am in a bowl
I am a fruit
I grow on trees
What am I?

Answer: A pear.

Kayla Pitura (6)
Heron Hill Primary School, Kendal

What Am I?

I have grey fur
I am soft
You find me in trees
I make a weird sound
I live in Australia
What am I?

Answer: A koala.

Lily Pearson (6)
Heron Hill Primary School, Kendal

Flutter

I can fly
I am very nice
I give you money
I am very sparkly and magical
I hold a wand
What am I?

Answer: A fairy.

Phoebe Mackereth (6)
Heron Hill Primary School, Kendal

Big-Mouthed Animal

I like to eat water lilies
You can find me at the zoo
I like to be in the water
I am grey
What am I?

Answer: A hippo.

Alec Birch-Rushworth (6)
Heron Hill Primary School, Kendal

What Am I?

I have wings
I breathe fire
I have scales
I am red
I live in castles and mountains
What am I?

Answer: A dragon.

Max Carter (5)
Heron Hill Primary School, Kendal

Magical Creature

It looks like a horse
It has a horn
It has a medium tail
It lives in magical lands
What is it?

Answer: A unicorn.

Amelia Mawson (6)
Heron Hill Primary School, Kendal

Roar

I have stripes
I am orange
My favourite food is meat and people
I have blue eyes
What am I?

Answer: A tiger.

Jessica Fishwick (6)
Heron Hill Primary School, Kendal

The Carrot Muncher

I am brown and fluffy
I can hop
I can be a pet
My favourite food is carrots
What am I?

Answer: A rabbit.

Seren Birch (5)
Heron Hill Primary School, Kendal

What Am I?

I don't like cats
I like people
I like to eat my dad's slippers
What am I?

Answer: A dog.

Kassius Venning (6)
Heron Hill Primary School, Kendal

Slow And Lazy

I live around trees
I am normally grey and brown
I am really slow
I eat leaves
I look like a person
But just with a furry body
I have really weird eyes
I don't walk on the ground much
I have very strong hands
What am I?

Answer: A sloth.

Charlotte Mackenzie (7)
King Charles CE Primary School, Falmouth

A Beautiful Animal

I come in beautiful black but also sunshine mustard-yellow
On my pretty black coat I have some round jaguar-like spots on me
I climb and sleep on damp trees in the Amazon
I am a big fluffy cat
I have green glaring eyes
I roar
What am I?

Answer: A panther.

Emily Searle (7)
King Charles CE Primary School, Falmouth

On My Lawn

I am very colourful and bright
I can be big
I can be small
Sometimes I'm not even there at all
I die in winter
I grow in summer
I grow things on me
What am I?

Answer: A flower.

Ruben Kahane (7)
King Charles CE Primary School, Falmouth

Creepy

I am black
I am scary
There are lots of different types of me
I run really fast
I am really hairy
I like to hide
I have eight legs
I shoot webs
What am I?

Answer: A spider.

Braxton-Heath Boots (7)
King Charles CE Primary School, Falmouth

A Handy Container

I am helpful
I can be smooth or bumpy
I can be small or big
There are lots of different ways to open me
Sometimes I have a lid
I have water in me
What am I?

Answer: A water bottle.

Ethan Hill (7)
King Charles CE Primary School, Falmouth

The Fluffy

I live in the sky
I'm fluffy
I am white
I can come in every shape and size
I look like marshmallows
I go in the night and come in the day
What am I?

Answer: A cloud.

Beatrice Cavender (6)
King Charles CE Primary School, Falmouth

A Trick

I can be written
I can be told
I can be read
I can be written in any colour
I can be shown
I can be typed
I can be solved
What am I?

Answer: A riddle.

Sam Kahane (7)
King Charles CE Primary School, Falmouth

My Beautiful Bug

I have wavy antennae just like the wind
I have short legs that tickle you when I walk
I hide my wings until it's time to flutter
through the bright sky
I can be lots of colours such as yellow, red,
orange and blue
Gardeners love me and I am as spotty as a
leopard
What am I?

Answer: A ladybird.

Annabelle Parker (7)
Purley CE Primary School, Purley On Thames

Marching Soldier

I may be small but I am strong
My six legs are quick and march with my
friends
I can be brown, black or red
I don't have ears but hear through my feet
I don't have lungs but breathe through my
skin
I protect my queen
What am I?

Answer: An ant.

Freya Eldred (6)
Purley CE Primary School, Purley On Thames

Lengthy Limbs

I creep around your house
I'm not deadly so do not worry
I'm as dark as night
I have as many legs as a spider
I have lengthy long limbs
I'm a father
What am I?

Answer: A daddy-long-legs.

Brandon Pollard (7)

Purley CE Primary School, Purley On Thames

A Hopper

My minibeast eats grass and wheat
It loves making noise with its feet
It is a pest in a crowd and can get very loud
It prefers living outside in the heat
What is it?

Answer: A grasshopper.

Lewis Tovey (7)
Purley CE Primary School, Purley On Thames

What Can I Be?

I waggle when I want to talk
I visit lots of flowers
A girl is my leader
I like making sweet things
I live with lots of brothers
I am yellow and black
What am I?

Answer: A bee.

Phoebe Tovey (6)
Purley CE Primary School, Purley On Thames

In The Woods

I live in the woods
I eat grass
I am very shy
I run very fast
I am brown
I have four brown legs
I have brown fur
I have a short tail
I drink water from a lake
I have little eyes
I have long antlers
What am I?

Answer: A deer.

Elsie Butcher (6)
Shirland Primary School, Shirland

The Tree Huggers

I have a fluffy tail
I have fluffy legs
I have soft arms
I have a soft body
I have a fluffy head
I like hanging on trees
I have soft ears
I live in Australia
What am I?

Answer: A koala.

Sophie Vickers (6)
Shirland Primary School, Shirland

The Small Creature

I have lots of legs
I crawl around
I like to eat apples
I am small and long
I turn into something else
My small hair tickles your hand
What am I?

Answer: A caterpillar.

Chelsea Neilson (6)
Shirland Primary School, Shirland

The Furball

I am fluffy
I am soft
I like to chase mice
I like to play outside
I like milk
I like meat
I like to play with my ball
What am I?

Answer: A cat.

Millie-Grace Ryan (6)
Shirland Primary School, Shirland

Endangered Animals

I have green eyes
I have black fur
I like eating animals
I am good at climbing
I can run fast
I come out at dawn
What am I?

Answer: A black jaguar.

Joseph Lee (6)
Shirland Primary School, Shirland

Jungle Poem

I live in the jungle
I have sharp claws
I have four legs
I am black
I can climb
I hunt for food
What am I?

Answer: A panther.

Harry Fletcher (6)
Shirland Primary School, Shirland

My Mystery Poem

I have soft fur
I have four legs
I have short ears
I have a spotty body
I have a long neck
What am I?

Answer: A giraffe.

Keira Vickers (6)
Shirland Primary School, Shirland

The Dark Creature

I hang up at night
I might give you a fright
I have two wings
I having glowing yellow eyes
What am I?

Answer: A bat.

Finley Bradshaw (6)
Shirland Primary School, Shirland

The Green Mystery

I live in a pond
I can jump
I have two long legs
I have a long tongue
I eat flies
What am I?

Answer: A frog.

Logan Jones (6)
Shirland Primary School, Shirland

Feeling Blue

I sometimes have a little glitter.
I also go round the bend.
I have two banks but have no cash.
I always fall but never smash.
What am I?

Answer: A river.

Robin Arbuthnott (6)
St Barnabas Primary School, Oxford

What Am I?

I have shiny clean fins
I love to swim around
I live in the ocean
I love playing with my ocean friends
I like looking at everyone's pattern
I love being myself
What am I?

Answer: A mermaid.

Mia Brailsford (6)
St Dunstan's RC Primary School, Moston

The Speedy Cat

I am amazing
I can reach speeds of over 60mph
I am a mammal
I am a carnivore
I live in the grasslands of Africa
I am well camouflaged because of my
spotty coat
What am I?

Answer: A cheetah.

Ermiyas Kifle (6)
St Dunstan's RC Primary School, Moston

Colourful Animal

I am green
I can change colour
I eat little bugs
You can see me in the jungle
I have a curly tail
I have a very sticky and stretchy tongue
What am I?

Answer: A chameleon.

Fiyinfoluwa Ibitoye (6)
St Dunstan's RC Primary School, Moston

Playful Pet

I am fast
I love to eat ham
I sit in the sun
I love to go for walks
I enjoy delicious bones
I have lots of energy
I am a loving friend
What am I?

Answer: A dog.

Finley Lamour (6)
St Dunstan's RC Primary School, Moston

Scary Animal

I am a herbivore
I have two sharp horns
I am a mammal
I have two pointy ears
I am grey and dry
If I'm angry I will charge
What am I?

Answer: A rhino.

Hosieo Selemon (6)
St Dunstan's RC Primary School, Moston

No Legs

I am long
I am purple
I like to slide on a rock
I like to eat leaves
I like to go somewhere
I like to slither around
What am I?

Answer: A snake.

Rae Toner (5)
St Dunstan's RC Primary School, Moston

What Am I?

I am the king of the jungle
I roar
I eat meat
I have a hairy mane
I have sharp teeth
My babies are cubs
What am I?

Answer: I am a lion.

Emilia Ajayi Usman (6)
St Dunstan's RC Primary School, Moston

The Best Pet Ever!

I have a long tail
I don't like water
I like to drink milk
I say meow
I live with an owner
They love me
What am I?

Answer: A cat.

Charlotte Lodge (6)
St Dunstan's RC Primary School, Moston

Leaf Eater

I live in Africa
I have a pattern on my body
I have a long neck
I am tall like a skyscraper
I am a herbivore
What am I?

Answer: A giraffe.

David Omanua (6)
St Dunstan's RC Primary School, Moston

Fluffy Friend

I have soft fur
I eat carrots
I am pink
I jump
I have two teeth
I put my teeth out
What am I?

Answer: I am a rabbit.

Bernice Agbontaen (6)
St Dunstan's RC Primary School, Moston

Green Biter

I am green
I can hiss
I am long
I have sharp teeth
I have no legs
I can wiggle
What am I?

Answer: A snake.

Oscar Whittaker (6)
St Dunstan's RC Primary School, Moston

Key Workers Are Heroes

If you see that car
Don't leave the scene, you won't go far
If you're lost, you won't pay the cost
If you go in jail, you will turn pale
They work at night
To see if everything is alright
They go away at day
They catch them in the hatch
If you see the choppers
Beware of the coppers
They go in the car
To get to the doughnut bar
Who are they?

Answer: The police.

Zach Sproit (7)
The Phoenix Primary School, Laindon

Key Workers

This key worker needs to drive
To save peoples lives
This key worker does people's dishes
To talk about people's wishes
This key worker loves to chat about
Last people's facts
This key worker gets people dressed
To make them look their best
This key worker makes people tea
Because they are a busy bee
This key worker makes people supper
They will even brew you your cuppa
This key worker helps to keep you well
And has picked you up as you fell
This key worker takes you to the bath
And takes you along the path

Ths key worker does your washing to keep
you clean
And polishes your side with Mr Sheen.
Who is it?

Answer: A carer.

Georgia McDonald (7)
The Phoenix Primary School, Laindon

NHS

They save lives
If you see them give them a high five
They look after your heart
They are as smart as a tart
If you have a cold they make you put on a
sweater
They help people with a needle
If you have hurt your knee
They will be as busy as a bee
They take your blood to keep you at your
best
They give you medicine to help your
skeleton
Who are they?

Answer: Doctors.

Jake Maynard (7)
The Phoenix Primary School, Laindon

Thank You Key Workers

They make you like a busy bee
They take care of us more than a bunny
When they are dressed they are the best
They can chat with you while they wait
They will never turn up late
They can make supper like a butler
They can chat like a bat
They can make you a perfect cupper after
your supper.
Who are they?

Answer: Our carers.

Damian Phillips (7)

The Phoenix Primary School, Laindon

Thank You Key Workers

They check the speed with cameras
They have to work all day and night
They have a lay
They have a tea
Like a buzzy bee
They have a bar so the bad guys cannot escape
They have a fast car called a Panda with bars
The scene they will not get far
Who are they?

Answer: The police.

Oliver Rose (7)
The Phoenix Primary School, Laindon

What Am I?

I have a pointy nose
I chatter with my friends
I have a blowhole on my smooth grey head
You will find me diving through the
turquoise ocean
I am one of the most intelligent of
mammals on Planet Earth
I leap above the wavy crystal-clear ocean
What am I?

Answer: A dolphin.

Summer Riggs (6), Aleksandra Padron (6), Imani Hills Powell (7), Freya King (6), Ava (7) & Kadian Richardson (6)
The Phoenix Primary School, Laindon

What Am I?

I have a round nose
I chatter with my friends
I have a blowhole on my smooth grey head
You will find me diving through the
turquoise ocean
I am one of the most intelligent of
mammals on Planet Earth
I leap above the wavy crystal-clear ocean
What am I?

Answer: A dolphin.

Danilas Subonis (7)
The Phoenix Primary School, Laindon

What Am I?

I live in the deep, navy blue salty sea
I have black beady eyes
My skin is smooth and silvery like the moon
in the midnight sky
I am a hungry carnivore that hunts cute
seals
I am a bloodthirsty vicious predator
I have needle-sharp teeth
What am I?

Answer: A shark.

Nkiere Along (6), Tadas Vaisnoras (7), Devon Regan (6), Charley & Adanna Nwaiwu (6)
The Phoenix Primary School, Laindon

Thank You Key Workers

If you see their car, don't run, you won't get far!
If you're in jail you might see their mail
If you succeed this is not a good deed
If it is night they use a light
If you get chased by a chopper you might see a copper
Who are they?

Answer: A policeman.

Frankie Fayers (7)
The Phoenix Primary School, Laindon

Thank You Key Workers

This person wears a fire-proof suit
This person climbs a ladder to get to a fire
They go down a pole which is through a hole
This person sprays a hose to put the fire in a doze
This person saves people and climbs as high as a steeple
Who is it?

Answer: A fireman.

Alexis-Rose White (7)

The Phoenix Primary School, Laindon

What Am I?

I can swing high and low
I can use my body like the drums
I protect my own with my big, long, hairy arms
Some could say my hands are bigger than a human
I have more attitude than a teenager
I am not as bright looking as most
What am I?

Answer: A gorilla.

Archie Stevens (7)
The Phoenix Primary School, Laindon

What Am I?

You will find me in jagged hard rocks
Or on the sand that is golden
I make a tasty sea snack
You might mistake me for a seashell
I carry my rock-hard home on my back
I scurry sideways
I can give a sharp pinch
What am I?

Answer: A crab.

Bella Fairclough (6)
The Phoenix Primary School, Laindon

What Am I?

I am a big type of cat
I live in the jungle
I have patches
I am a carnivore
I have a tail
I have claws
I am a predator
The food I like to eat are gazelles and zebras
What am I?

Answer: A cheetah.

Daniel Ojedele (7)
The Phoenix Primary School, Laindon

Can You Guess What I Am?

I live in the sea
I can squeeze into small spaces
I can be different colours
I have suckers
I can turn the water black
I have eight legs
What am I?

Answer: An octopus.

Ollie Amiable (7)
The Phoenix Primary School, Laindon

What Am I?

I am brown and furry
I am famous
I have spots
I am in lots of movies for kids
My name also means expensive
What am I?

Answer: A deer.

Kyra Kudjoe-Swan (7)
The Phoenix Primary School, Laindon

What Am I?

I live in cold places
I am white
I eat fish
I have four legs
I camouflage against the snow
What am I?

Answer: A polar bear.

Faye Simons (7)
The Phoenix Primary School, Laindon

What Am I?

I live in a desert
I am hairy
I can change colour
I have eight legs
What am I?

Answer: A tarantula.

Lilyray Cahill (7)
The Phoenix Primary School, Laindon

Can You Guess What Animal I Am?

I have spots
I am a type of big cat
I have a tail
I can run very fast
What am I?

Answer: A cheetah.

Natalie Caddy (7)
The Phoenix Primary School, Laindon

What Am I?

I live on land and water
I eat fish
I like to swim a lot
I like to play
What am I?

Answer: A seal.

Riley Hayter (7)
The Phoenix Primary School, Laindon

The One-Legged Feathery Friend

I live on many continents including Africa
and both Americas.
Like all birds I have two legs
But I decide to stand on one.
My one egg lies in a muddy nest.
My favourite snacks are shrimp, snails and
algae.
The colours of my feathers depend on what
I eat.
I fly over the water with my ginormous
wings.
What am I?

Answer: A flamingo.

Isla McNaughton (6)
The Ursuline Preparatory School, Ilford

Reptile Riddle

I move very slowly
I live on land
I like to eat plants
Even though I have no hands
I am cold-blooded and live in a shell
I can live to one hundred years as well
I have no ears or tail
But that does not mean I am a snail
I am green but not that mean
What am I?

Answer: A tortoise.

Maliha Dearing (6)
The Ursuline Preparatory School, Ilford

The Joker

He has a laugh that makes you want to barf
His spots are black and he may just attack
His tail is sharp as a nail
He has lots of teeth
And his baby is called Keith
Be careful of this dangerous mammal
And instead ride a camel
What is it?

Answer: A hyena.

Isla Rose Pearson (6)

The Ursuline Preparatory School, Ilford

A Riddle And A Rhyme

I can travel at high speed
I am very fast
The things I am made of are hard and
strong
Sometimes you see me
Sometimes you don't
I can get very hot
I often leave a trail
Bright and shiny... that's me
What am I?

Answer: A meteor.

Rishaan Sharma (6)

The Ursuline Preparatory School, Ilford

The Love Bird

She is pink and she likes to blink
Her neck is long like a swan
This bird has thin legs and she lays eggs
She eats shrimp for her food
So leave her alone, dude
This love bird sings with her wings
What is she?

Answer: A flamingo.

Leyla Pearson (6)
The Ursuline Preparatory School, Ilford

What Am I?

I am round
There is one of me in your house
I can come in different colours
I can come in different shapes
I have hands but no fingers
I can tell people things but do not have a mouth
What am I?

Answer: A clock.

Zakariya Patel (5)
The Ursuline Preparatory School, Ilford

What Am I?

I am tall
I have four legs
I have spots
I eat trees
I have a black tongue
I have a bit of white on me
I am in Africa
My babies are bigger than you
I have hooves
I have black eyes
What am I?

Answer: A giraffe.

Harry Hodgson (6)
Unity College Nursery, Blackpool

What Am I?

I have four legs
I have no hands
I am black and white
I have nine lives
I have two eyes
I have a tail
I have thirty teeth
I have two ears
I drink milk
What am I?

Answer: A cat.

Jacobe Cunningham (7)
Unity College Nursery, Blackpool

What Am I?

I have no legs
I have scales
You will find me in a forest
My favourite food is some bugs
I have a long tail
My tongue splits into to two
What am I?

Answer: A snake.

Lucas Algar (6)
Unity College Nursery, Blackpool

What Am I?

I live in the jungle
I am furry and hairy
At night it is hard to spot me
I have four legs
I eat crocodiles
My favourite thing is water
What am I?

Answer: A jaguar.

Jayden McCreadie (7)
Unity College Nursery, Blackpool

What Am I?

I have two pointy ears
A very long neck
My favourite food is leaves off the trees
You will see me coming because I am
orange and yellow
What am I?

Answer: A giraffe.

Lola Mitchell (6)
Unity College Nursery, Blackpool

What Am I?

You can find me in Africa
You can see my grey skin
I have two ears
You can see my trunk
What am I?

Answer: An elephant.

Darci-Mae Gibson (6)
Unity College Nursery, Blackpool

Young**Writers**
Est.1991

YOUNG WRITERS
INFORMATION

We hope you have enjoyed reading this book – and that you will continue to in the coming years.

If you're a young writer who enjoys reading and creative writing, or the parent of an enthusiastic poet or story writer, do visit our website **www.youngwriters.co.uk**. Here you will find free competitions, workshops and games, as well as recommended reads, a poetry glossary and our blog.

If you would like to order further copies of this book, or any of our other titles, then please give us a call or visit **www.youngwriters.co.uk**.

Young Writers
Remus House
Coltsfoot Drive
Peterborough
PE2 9BF
(01733) 890066
info@youngwriters.co.uk